ACHIEVE

Year
6

D0185135

# Grammar, Spelling and Punctuation

## SATs Practice Papers

**Marie Lallaway
& Madeleine Barnes**

RISING★STARS

Although every effort has been made to ensure that website addresses are correct at time of going to press, Rising Stars cannot be held responsible for the content of any website mentioned in this book. It is sometimes possible to find a relocated web page by typing in the address of the home page for a website in the URL window of your browser.

Hachette UK's policy is to use papers that are natural, renewable and recyclable products and made from wood grown in sustainable forests. The logging and manufacturing processes are expected to conform to the environmental regulations of the country of origin.

Orders: please contact Bookpoint Ltd, 130 Park Drive, Milton Park, Abingdon, Oxon OX14 4SE. Telephone: (44) 01235 400555. Email: primary@bookpoint.co.uk.

Lines are open from 9 a.m. to 5 p.m., Monday to Saturday, with a 24-hour message answering service. Visit our website at www.risingstars-uk.com for details of the full range of Rising Stars publications.

Online support and queries email: onlinesupport@risingstars-uk.com.

ISBN: 978 1 51044 291 7

© Rising Stars UK Ltd 2018

This edition published in 2018 by Rising Stars UK Ltd
First published in 2015 by Rising Stars UK Ltd
Rising Stars UK Ltd, part of Hodder Education Group
An Hachette UK Company
Carmelite House
50 Victoria Embankment
London EC4Y 0DZ

www.risingstars-uk.com

Impression number 10 9 8 7 6 5 4 3 2 1

Year 2022 2021 2020 2019 2018

Authors: Marie Lallaway and Madeleine Barnes

Series Editor: Madeleine Barnes

Accessibility Reviewer: Vivien Kilburn

Educational Adviser: Josh Lury

Cover design: Burville-Riley Partnership

Typeset in India

Printed in the UK

A catalogue record for this title is available from the British Library.

# Contents

The answers and spelling transcripts can be found in a pull-out section in the middle of this book.

# Introduction

## About the Practice Papers for Grammar, Punctuation and Spelling

The tests are written to cover the content domain of the *Key Stage 2 English grammar, punctuation and spelling test framework for the National Curriculum tests from 2016* (Standards & Testing Agency, 2015). The tests **as a whole** provide complete coverage of the content domain.

There are six papers in total: three assessing grammar, punctuation and vocabulary strategies (as per *Paper 1: questions* from the National Tests) and three assessing spelling (as per *Paper 2: spelling* from the National Tests).

The tests are intended for use during the spring and summer terms of Year 6 in preparation for the National Tests. Test demand increases within each test, as in the National Tests, so initial questions are easier than those towards the end of each test.

## How to use the Practice Papers

### Preparation and timings
1   Help your child prepare for each paper by simulating test conditions.
2   Ensure your child is seated appropriately in front of the paper they are going to work on.
3   Your child will need pens or pencils and erasers.
4   There are no time limits for the tests but you should be guided by the timings of the actual tests in relation to the number of marks available. Help with reading may be given using the same rules as when providing a reader with the Key Stage 2 tests.

*Spelling task*: Introduce your child to the test by telling them that you will read out each sentence including the missing word. You will then say the missing word. Finally, you will repeat the whole sentence.

• Your child will need to write the missing words in the spaces on their answer sheets.
• Your child should make their best attempts at the spelling, even for words that may be unfamiliar.
• The full scripts for the spelling tests are provided in the answer section which can be found in a pull-out section in the middle of this book.

## Supporting children during the tests

Before the tests, explain to your child that each test is an opportunity to show what they know, understand and can do. They should try to answer all the questions but should not worry if there are some they can't do.

Many children will be able to work independently in the tests, with minimal support. However, children should be encouraged to 'have a go' at a question, or to move on to a fresh question if they appear to be stuck. If they have time at the end of the test, they can come back to questions they have missed out.

## Marking the tests

Use the mark scheme and your own judgement to award marks. Do not award half marks. Note that a number of questions in each test may require children to do more than one thing for one mark. The mark scheme provides clear guidance in the allocation of marks to support consistent marking of the tests.

It is useful for your child to mark their own test questions from time to time. Your child can look at the test sheets and mark them as you read out the question and answer. You will need to check that your child is marking accurately. This approach also provides an opportunity to recap on any questions that your child found difficult to answer.

Further guidance on marking is available on page 60.

Keep track of your child's score using the table on the inside back cover of this book.

| Name: | Class: | Date: | Total marks: | /50 |
|---|---|---|---|---|

# Test 1, Paper 1: questions

**1** Circle the words that should have **capital letters** in the sentence below.

Each year in april, we take gifts to our grandparents in

scotland for their birthdays.

1 mark

**2** Tick one box in each row to show whether the sentence is a **statement** or a **command**.

1 mark

| Sentence | Statement | Command |
|---|---|---|
| Today, the train will leave earlier than usual. | | |
| Tomorrow, go to your grandma's after school. | | |
| Yesterday, we climbed a tree. | | |
| Bring your sports kit for the match this afternoon. | | |

**3** Circle the **relative pronoun** in the sentence below.

The new girl who started our school today is coming to our house later.

1 mark

/3

*Total for this page*

6

**4** Which **preposition** can complete both sentences?

Write the preposition in the box below.

I travel _____ home to school on the bus each day.

You must follow the treasure hunt clues _____ the start to the finish.

word: [            ]

1 mark

**5** What is the grammatical term for the underlined word?

Anita's idea was interesting but <u>impossible</u>.

Tick **one**.

noun [ ]

adjective [ ]

adverb [ ]

preposition [ ]

1 mark

**6** Underline the longest possible **noun phrase** in the sentence below.

Have you seen the new climbing frame in the playground?

1 mark

/ 3

*Total for this page*

7

**7** Circle the correct **verb form** to complete the sentence below.

are being     have been     are     will have been

Max and Jensen _____ best friends since they started school.

1 mark

**8** Write the question below as a **command**.

Remember to punctuate your answer correctly.

Can you open the window as it is very hot?

_____

1 mark

**9** Circle all the **nouns** in the sentence below.

Jess was asked to share her ideas about having more healthy food in school.

1 mark

/3

*Total for this page*

**10** Rewrite the sentence below, using correct **capital letters**.

on monday we will visit buckingham palace.

_____

1 mark

**11** Circle the correct **verb forms** to complete these sentences.

| is working/has worked/worked |

Mr Oliver _____ in the factory since it first opened and is still here today.

| tries/has tried/tried |

Samara _____ her best in the races yesterday.

| make/have made/making |

We _____ cakes to share with you all now.

1 mark

**12** Underline the **objects** in the sentences below.

Holly threw the ball.

Grandad pushed the wheelbarrow.

Can you catch it?

1 mark

/3

*Total for this page*

**13** Insert a **subordinating conjunction** to show that we swam in the river and played games at the same time.

We played games _____ we swam in the river.

1 mark

**14** Circle all the **pronouns** in the sentence below.

Oscar made a model castle from old boxes his dad had given him.

1 mark

**15** Insert a **comma** in the correct place in the sentence below.

Full of wonder we all gazed at the shooting star.

1 mark

/3

*Total for this page*

**16** Draw a line to match each word with its **synonym**.

| | |
|---|---|
| swift | secure |
| fasten | concern |
| immerse | soak |
| issue | rapid |

1 mark

**17** Tick one box in each row to show whether the sentences are written in the **active** or the **passive voice**.

| Sentence | Active | Passive |
|---|---|---|
| The seals were fed from a bucket of fish. | | |
| Kangaroos use their tails to balance. | | |
| Some trees are planted by squirrels burying nuts. | | |

1 mark

**18** Draw a line to match each **prefix** with the correct word.

| | |
|---|---|
| im | legal |
| ir | possible |
| in | responsible |
| il | attentive |

1 mark

/ 3

*Total for this page*

11

**19** Which is the correct way to write the sentence below as **reported speech**?

"Butterflies can see only three colours," said Anna.

1 mark

Tick **one**.

Anna said, that butterflies could see only three colours. ☐

Anna said that "butterflies can see only three colours." ☐

Anna says "that butterflies can see only three colours." ☐

Anna said that butterflies can see only three colours. ☐

**20** Rewrite the sentence below using **Standard English** to correct the underlined word.

1 mark

Remember to punctuate your answer correctly.

Can I have one of <u>them</u> cakes?

_____

**21** Circle the word that shows the event is **most likely** to happen.

1 mark

**definitely    perhaps    possibly    probably**

Nafeesah will _____ become an acrobat when she grows up.

/3

*Total for this page*

**22** Add an **adverbial phrase** to the sentence below.

_____, I always clean my teeth.

1 mark

**23** Tick the box to show which part of this sentence is a **relative clause**.

Long, long ago there lived a wonderful, flying creature

☐       ☐                    ☐

that guarded the magical mountain.

☐

1 mark

**24** What is the grammatical term for the underlined words in the sentence below?

The storm caused a lot of damage when it struck last night.

Tick **one**.

as a main clause                    ☐

as a noun phrase                    ☐

as a preposition phrase            ☐

as a relative clause                 ☐

1 mark

/3

*Total for this page*

13

**25** Write the **contracted form** of the underlined words in the box.

"You <u>should have</u> gone to bed earlier," my mum said.

1 mark

**26** Rewrite the sentence below as **direct speech**.

Remember to punctuate your sentence correctly.

The scientist said that she was pleased with her discovery.

1 mark

**27** Tick the **verb** that is written in the **past progressive form** in the passage below.

The stars were twinkling in the sky as Jodie gazed upwards and

1 mark

made a wish. It had been a lovely day.

/3

*Total for this page*

**28** Insert a **semi-colon** in the correct place in the sentence below.

There was a parade in the road outside school we all went out to have a look.

1 mark

**29** In the sentence below, Dad planted the flowers in the garden before the dog dug them up.

Write the verb in the **past perfect form** in the gap.

to plant

In the morning, Dad _____ lots of new flowers in the garden but the dog dug them up looking for its buried bone.

1 mark

**30** Explain how removing the **comma** changes the meaning of the sentence.

Let's play chase, Kate.

Let's play chase Kate.

_____

_____

_____

1 mark

/ 3

*Total for this page*

(15)

**31** Add the correct word from the box to complete the sentence below in the **subjunctive form.**

1 mark

> listened
>
> listen
>
> listening
>
> listens

The flying instructor recommended that Josh _____ carefully to all the information.

**32** Tick one sentence that is correctly punctuated.

1 mark

Tick **one**.

Venus – the brightest planet in our sky – can sometimes be seen without a telescope. ☐

The tallest volcano – at 27 km high, in fact – in the Solar System is on Mars. ☐

In 1846 – Neptune, the planet – was discovered. ☐

Many astronomers – believe that Mercury – was once a much larger planet. ☐

/ 2

*Total for this page*

**33** Tick the option that must end with an **exclamation mark**.

Tick **one**.

Give it to me ☐

Can you believe that we won ☐

What an amazing friend you are ☐

Sit down ☐

1 mark

**34** Circle the word in the passage that contains an apostrophe for **possession**.

Now that he's here, I'll book the taxi. We can pick up

Elsie from Fred's house.

1 mark

**35** Circle the **two** words that are **antonyms** in the sentence below.

The teacher completed the register to record

who was present or absent.

1 mark

/3

*Total for this page*

17

**36** Which sentence is written using **Standard English**?

Tick **one**.

1 mark

I done my exercises in the park. ☐

They was all late for assembly. ☐

I swam with the school team in the competition. ☐

You been here for three hours. ☐

**37** What is the **word class** of the underlined words in the sentence below?

1 mark

<u>The</u> boy put <u>three</u> drinks in <u>a</u> bag.

_____

**38** Replace the underlined word or words in the sentence below with the correct **pronouns**.

1 mark

Mr Lavin told the children to line up and <u>Mr Lavin</u> checked that

the <u>children</u> were all there.

/3

*Total for this page*

**39** What is the **subject** of the sentence below?

Last Wednesday, Luke went to Manchester to see Ellie.

Tick **one**.

Wednesday ☐

Manchester ☐

Luke ☐

Ellie ☐

1 mark

**40** Circle the **relative pronoun** in the sentence below.

My uncle, who was a famous ice-skater, has moved to America.

1 mark

**41** Rearrange the words in the statement below to make it a **question**.

Use only the given words.

Remember to punctuate your sentence correctly.

**Statement:** They are waiting for the train.

**Question:** _____

1 mark

/3

*Total for this page*  (19)

**42** Which sentence uses the **colon** correctly?

Tick **one**.

1 mark

I bought: some new stationery pencils, a ruler,
a selection of pens and a pencil case. ☐

I bought some new stationery: pencils, a ruler,
a selection of pens and a pencil case. ☐

I bought some new: stationery pencils, a ruler,
a selection of pens and a pencil case. ☐

I bought some new stationery pencils: a ruler,
a selection of pens and a pencil case. ☐

**43** Tick **two** boxes to show where the **inverted commas** should go.

Freddie told me to put it there, interrupted Pritika .

☐  ☐  ☐  ☐

1 mark

**44** Which underlined group of words is a **subordinate clause**?

Tick **one**.

1 mark

This is the best place I have ever been. ☐

Because you are late, we have changed the song! ☐

I didn't want to stay in the hotel for three days. ☐

Would you like a drink of milk or water? ☐

/3

Total for
this page

**45** Which **punctuation mark** should be used in the place indicated by the arrow?

Aradhya loved many different sports her favourites were

swimming and tennis.

Tick **one**.

comma ☐

semi-colon ☐

full stop ☐

hyphen ☐

1 mark

**46** Circle the **adverb** in the sentence below.

We are hoping to visit Gran's lovely home soon.

1 mark

**47** Insert one **comma** in the correct place in the sentence below.

Last Wednesday we won the singing competition at

the town hall.

1 mark

/ 3

*Total for this page*

(21)

**48** Insert a pair of **brackets** in the correct place in the sentence below.

The largest river in the world is the Amazon River 6,992 km in South America.

1 mark

**49** Complete each sentence below with a word formed from the root word <u>enjoy</u>.

The party was a very _____ experience.

She got incredible _____ from reading adventure stories.

1 mark

**50** Circle the two **conjunctions** in the sentence below.

I really wanted to go to the concert, but I realised that I didn't have my ticket or my phone with me!

1 mark

/3

*Total for this page*

| Name: | Class: | Date: | Total marks: | /20 |
|---|---|---|---|---|

# Test 1, Paper 2: spelling

1   We are _____ the bulbs from their pots to the garden.  ☐

2   There was a _____ response to your idea.  ☐

3   The new road has made a _____ difference to the traffic problem.  ☐

4   To bake bread, you first need to make a _____.  ☐

5   We have designed an _____ programme for the concert.  ☐

6   Our snake is growing in _____ each month.  ☐

7   The _____ has introduced a new law.  ☐

8   My favourite book is full of _____ stories.  ☐

9   Your dentist will _____ you on how to care for your teeth.  ☐

10   It is helpful if your dog is trained to be _____.  ☐

11   There was an _____ pause after Tom's joke.  ☐

12   The rope should be _____ up tidily after you use it.  ☐

13   It is _____ to wear a safety helmet in the caves.  ☐

14   They _____ through the night to arrive on time.  ☐

15   That is a lovely _____ of fabric.  ☐

16   There was a _____ smell in the garden shed.  ☐

17   I went to the doctor because I had a _____.  ☐

18   When I was on holiday, we sailed to an _____.  ☐

19   It is very important that you eat a _____ lunch.  ☐

20   My Dad found the idea quite _____.  ☐

| Name: | Class: | Date: | Total marks: | /50 |

# Test 2, Paper 1: questions

**1** Write the **contracted form** of the underlined words in the box.

I told Joe that <u>he had</u> won first prize.

[ ]

1 mark

**2** Circle the words in the sentence that should have **capital letters**.

On friday we will go to molly's house for tea.

1 mark

**3** Insert an appropriate **adverb** to complete the sentence below.

The ducklings swam _____ across the pond.

1 mark

/3

*Total for this page*

**4** Tick the sentences that correctly use the **possessive apostrophe**.

Can I borrow Jamila's bicycle? ☐

At the start of the race, all of the cars' engines were ☐
revving noisily.

The dog has lost it's ball. ☐

After the match, the teams' kit was filthy. ☐

☐
1 mark

**5** Tick the box to show where a **comma** should go.

If  you  enjoy  dancing  you  should  come  to  the  theatre  with  us
☐ ☐ ☐ ☐

this  evening.

☐
1 mark

**6** Complete the sentences below by writing the **conjunctions** from
the box in the correct place.

Use each conjunction only once.

| but | or | and |

Would you like to play inside _____ outside?

You will need a drink _____ a ticket, _____

you do not need to pay for them.

☐
1 mark

/3

*Total for
this page* 25

**7** Underline all the **verbs** in the sentence below.

Female lions do most of the hunting while the males patrol the territory and protect the group.

1 mark

**8** Write the correct **determiner**, <u>a</u> or <u>an</u>, in each gap below.

On our holiday, we arrived at _____ airport in the middle of nowhere and we were picked up by _____ ox and cart to take us to _____ train station.

1 mark

**9** Circle the verb in the **past perfect tense** to complete the sentence below.

When I arrived at the cinema, the film **started / had started / was starting / starts**.

1 mark

/3

*Total for this page*

**10** Which option is the correct **relative pronoun** for the sentence below?

The town _____ I live is close to the sea.

Tick **one**.

that ☐

where ☐

which ☐

who ☐

1 mark

**11** Write the verbs in the gaps in the **past progressive tense**.

to listen

Simon and Nikhil _____ to the radio while they

to build

_____ a model plane.

1 mark

**12** Which sentence is the most **formal**?

Tick **one**.

Daily exercise should be promoted for all. ☐

You should exercise every day. ☐

Exercising every day is a great idea. ☐

You really should try to exercise daily. ☐

1 mark

/3

*Total for this page*

**13** Tick **two** boxes to show where the **inverted commas** should go.

The mayor announced, This year's carnival procession will

⬜      ⬜      ⬜      ⬜

travel throughout the whole town.

⬜

1 mark

**14** Label the boxes with **N (noun)**, **A (adjective)**, **V (verb)** and **P (preposition)** to show the parts of the sentence.

"After the storm, the destruction left in the garden was

⬜      ⬜

completely awful," said one local.

⬜      ⬜

1 mark

**15** Explain why an **apostrophe** is used in the sentence below.

Everyone in the class liked Oscar's idea.

_____

_____

1 mark

/3

*Total for this page*

**16** Draw a line to match each word with its **suffix**.

| appoint | ful |
|---------|-----|
| bitter | less |
| hair | ness |
| dread | ment |

1 mark

**17** Elsie wants to know if the team are in the final round.

Write the **question** she could ask to find out.

Remember to punctuate your sentence correctly.

1 mark

**18** Underline one word in each sentence that shows that it is a **command**.

When the race starts, run as fast as you can.

If the alarm sounds, leave the building quickly and quietly.

1 mark

/3

*Total for this page*

**19** Why is a **comma** used in the sentence below?

Would you like to go to the park, the museum or the cinema?

Tick **one**.

to divide the sentence in two halves ☐

to introduce speech ☐

to mark a clause ☐

to separate items in a list ☐

1 mark

**20** Which word is the **antonym** of <u>combine</u>?

Tick **one**.

separate ☐

mix ☐

comfort ☐

descend ☐

1 mark

**21** Underline the **subject** of the sentence below.

The football manager posed for a photograph.

1 mark

/3

*Total for this page*

# Answers and spelling transcripts

## Test 1, Paper 1: questions

| Qu. | Content domain | Answer | Marking guidance | Mark |
|---|---|---|---|---|
| 1 | G5.1 – capital letters | circle: april; scotland | **1 mark** for **two** correct answers | 1 |
| 2 | G2.1 – statements; G2.3 – commands | (see table below) | **1 mark** for **four** correct answers | 1 |
| 3 | G1.5b – relative pronouns | circle: who | | 1 |
| 4 | G1.7 – prepositions | from | | 1 |
| 5 | G1.3 – adjectives | tick: adjective | | 1 |
| 6 | G3.2 – noun phrases | underline: the new climbing frame in the playground | All of the noun phrase must be underlined – no more, no less. | 1 |
| 7 | G4.1b – verbs in perfect form | circle: have been | | 1 |
| 8 | G2.3 – commands | Open the window as it is very hot. OR Open the window. | Correct use of capital letter and full stop is required for the mark. | 1 |
| 9 | G1.1 – nouns | circle: Jess; ideas; food; school | **1 mark** for **four** correct answers | 1 |
| 10 | G5.1 – capital letters | On Monday we will visit Buckingham Palace. | **1 mark** for **four** correct answers | 1 |
| 11 | G4.1b – verbs in perfect form | circle: has worked; tried; have made | **1 mark** for **three** correct answers | 1 |
| 12 | G1.9 – subject and object | underline: the ball; the wheelbarrow; it | **1 mark** for **three** correct answers<br>**Also accept** answers that do not include 'the'. | 1 |
| 13 | G1.4 – conjunctions | **Accept** the correct insertion of an appropriate subordinating conjunction, e.g. while; whilst; as; when. | **Do not accept** misspellings of the subordinating conjunction. | 1 |
| 14 | G1.5 – pronouns | circle: his; him | **1 mark** for **two** correct answers | 1 |

Question 2 table:

| Sentence | Statement | Command |
|---|---|---|
| Today, the train will leave earlier than usual. | ✔ | |
| Tomorrow, go to your grandma's after school. | | ✔ |
| Yesterday, we climbed a tree. | ✔ | |
| Bring your sports kit for the match this afternoon. | | ✔ |

| 15 | G5.6b – commas after fronted adverbials | Full of wonder, we all gazed at the shooting star. | | 1 |
|---|---|---|---|---|
| 16 | G6.1 – synonyms and antonyms | swift     rapid<br>fasten    secure<br>immerse  soak<br>issue     concern | **1 mark** for **four** correct answers | 1 |

| 17 | G4.4 – passive and active | | | **1 mark** for **three** correct answers | 1 |
|---|---|---|---|---|---|

| Sentence | Active | Passive |
|---|---|---|
| The seals were fed from a bucket of fish. | | ✓ |
| Kangaroos use their tails to balance. | ✓ | |
| Some trees are planted by squirrels burying nuts. | | ✓ |

| 18 | G6.2 – prefixes | im   possible<br>ir    responsible<br>in   attentive<br>il    legal | **1 mark** for **four** correct answers | 1 |
|---|---|---|---|---|
| 19 | G5.7 – inverted commas | tick: Anna said that butterflies can see only three colours. | | 1 |
| 20 | G7.1 – Standard English | Can I have one of those/these/the cakes? | Capital letter and question mark use must be correct for **1 mark**. | 1 |
| 21 | G1.6 – adverbs | circle: definitely | | 1 |
| 22 | G1.6a – adverbials | **Accept** a suitable phrase that makes sense, e.g. *Every night*; *Early in the morning*; *Without being asked*. | **Do not accept** a subordinate clause, e.g. *When I get up*. | 1 |
| 23 | G3.1a – relative clauses | tick: that guarded the magical mountain. | | 1 |
| 24 | G3.1 – sentences and clauses | tick: as a main clause | | 1 |
| 25 | G5.8 – apostrophes | should've | | 1 |
| 26 | G5.7 – inverted commas | The scientist said, "I am pleased with my discovery." OR "I am pleased with my discovery," said the scientist. OR "I am pleased with my discovery." (without *the scientist said*). | Inverted commas, commas and full stops must be correctly placed. Capital letters must be used correctly. | 1 |
| 27 | G4.1d – present and past progressive | tick: were twinkling | | 1 |
| 28 | G5.11 – semi-colons | There was a parade in the road outside school; we all went out to have a look. | | 1 |
| 29 | G4.1b – verbs in perfect form | had planted | | 1 |

| 30 | G5.6a – commas to clarify meaning | **Accept** answers that explain that in the second sentence Kate will be chased, or that she is not being spoken to directly. For example, without the comma it means that they will chase Kate. | | 1 |
|---|---|---|---|---|
| 31 | G4.3 – subjunctive verb forms | listen | | 1 |
| 32 | G5.9 – punctuation for parenthesis | tick: Venus – the brightest planet in our sky – can sometimes be seen without a telescope. | | 1 |
| 33 | G2.4 – exclamations | tick: What an amazing friend you are | | 1 |
| 34 | G5.8 apostrophes | circle: Fred's | | 1 |
| 35 | G6.1 – synonyms and antonyms | circle: present, absent | | 1 |
| 36 | G7.1 – Standard English | tick: I swam with the school team in the competition. | | 1 |
| 37 | G1.8 – determiners | determiner(s) | | 1 |
| 38 | G1.5 – pronouns | he<br>we/they | **1 mark** for **two** correct answers | 1 |
| 39 | G1.9 – subject and object | tick: Luke | | 1 |
| 40 | G1.5b – relative pronouns | circle: who | | 1 |
| 41 | G2.2 – questions | Are they waiting for the train? | **Accept** answers that include a correctly formed question mark and include a capital letter.<br><br>**Do not accept** answers with omitted words or additional words. | 1 |
| 42 | G5.10 – colons | tick: I bought some new stationery: pencils, a ruler, a selection of pens and a pencil case. | | 1 |
| 43 | G5.7 – inverted commas | tick box before 'Freddie' and after 'there,' | **1 mark** for **two** correct answers | 1 |
| 44 | G3.4 – subordinating conjunctions and subordinate clauses | tick: <u>Because you are late</u>, we have changed the song! | | 1 |
| 45 | G5.11 – semi-colons | tick: semi-colon | | 1 |
| 46 | G1.6 – adverbs | circle: soon | | 1 |
| 47 | G5.6b – commas after fronted adverbials | Last Wednesday, we won the singing competition at the town hall. | Comma must be correctly formed. | 1 |

| 48 | G5.9 – punctuation for parenthesis | The largest river in the world is the Amazon River (6,992 km) in South America. | | 1 |
|---|---|---|---|---|
| 49 | G6.3 – suffixes | enjoyable<br>enjoyment | Must be correctly spelled and use a lower case letter. | 1 |
| 50 | G1.4 – conjunctions | circle: but, or | **1 mark** for **two** correct answers | 1 |

# Test 1, Paper 2: spelling task transcript

Spelling one: The word is **transplanting**.
We are **transplanting** the bulbs from their pots to the garden.

Spelling two: The word is **positive**.
There was a **positive** response to your idea.

Spelling three: The word is **considerable**.
The new road has made a **considerable** difference to the traffic problem.

Spelling four: The word is **dough**.
To bake bread, you first need to make a **dough**.

Spelling five: The word is **official**.
We have designed an **official** programme for the concert.

Spelling six: The word is **length**.
Our snake is growing in **length** each month.

Spelling seven: The word is **government**.
The **government** has introduced a new law.

Spelling eight: The word is **adventure**.
My favourite book is full of **adventure** stories.

Spelling nine: The word is **advise**.
Your dentist will **advise** you on how to care for your teeth.

Spelling ten: The word is **obedient**.
It is helpful if your dog is trained to be **obedient**.

Spelling eleven: The word is **awkward**.
There was an **awkward** pause after Tom's joke.

Spelling twelve: The word is **coiled**.
The rope should be **coiled** up tidily after you use it.

Spelling thirteen: The word is **necessary**.
It is **necessary** to wear a safety helmet in the caves.

Spelling fourteen: The word is **travelled**.
They **travelled** through the night to arrive on time.

Spelling fifteen: The word is **piece**.
That is a lovely **piece** of fabric.

Spelling sixteen: The word is **peculiar**.
There was a **peculiar** smell in the garden shed.

Spelling seventeen: The word is **cough**.
I went to the doctor because I had a **cough**.

Spelling eighteen: The word is **island**.
When I was on holiday, we sailed to an **island**.

Spelling nineteen: The word is **nutritious**.
It is very important that you eat a **nutritious** lunch.

Spelling twenty: The word is **inconceivable**.
My Dad found the idea quite **inconceivable**.

# Test 2, Paper 1: questions

| Qu. | Content domain | Answer | Marking guidance | Mark |
|---|---|---|---|---|
| 1 | G5.8 – apostrophes | he'd | **Do not accept** answers that omit or misplace the apostrophe. | 1 |
| 2 | G5.1 – capital letters | circle: friday; molly's | **1 mark** for **two** correct answers | 1 |
| 3 | G1.6 – adverbs | **Accept** an answer that is a plausible, correctly spelled adverb, e.g. *quickly; slowly; nervously; confidently.* | | 1 |
| 4 | G5.8 – apostrophes | tick: Can I borrow Jamila's bicycle?<br>At the start of the race, all of the cars' engines were revving noisily. | **1 mark** for **two** correct answers | 1 |
| 5 | G5.6a – commas to clarify meaning | tick box after: dancing | | 1 |

| 6 | G3.3 – coordinating conjunctions | or; and; but | **1 mark** for **three** correct answers | 1 |
|---|---|---|---|---|
| 7 | G1.2 – verbs | underline: do; patrol; protect | **1 mark** for **three** correct answers | 1 |
| 8 | G1.8 – determiners | an; an; a | **1 mark** for **three** correct answers | 1 |
| 9 | G4.1b – verbs in perfect form | circle: had started | | 1 |
| 10 | G1.5b – relative pronouns | tick: where | | 1 |
| 11 | G4.1d – present and past progressive | were listening; were building | **1 mark** for **two** correct answers | 1 |
| 12 | G7.2 - Formal and informal vocabulary, G7.3 - Formal and informal structures | tick: Daily exercise should be promoted for all. | | 1 |
| 13 | G5.7 – inverted commas | tick boxes after: announced; town | **1 mark** for **two** correct answers | 1 |
| 14 | G1.1 – nouns, G1.2 – verbs, G1.3 – adjectives, G1.7 – prepositions | destruction (N)   in (P)   awful (A)   said (V) | **1 mark** for **four** correct answers | 1 |
| 15 | G5.8 – apostrophes | **Accept** answers that refer to possession, e.g. the idea is from Oscar. | | 1 |
| 16 | G6.3 – suffixes | appoint     ment<br>bitter        ness<br>hair           less<br>dread        ful | **1 mark** for **four** correct answers | 1 |
| 17 | G2.2 - Questions, G5.3 - Question marks | **Accept** a grammatically correct and accurately punctuated question, e.g.<br>Is the team in the final round? OR<br>Are the team in the final? OR Do you know if the team are in the final round? | **Also accept** a correctly constructed and punctuated question that is enclosed in inverted commas.<br>**Do not accept** the addition of a reporting clause resulting in a question contained within a statement, Elsie asked, "Is the team in the final round?" | 1 |
| 18 | G2.3 – commands | underline: run; leave | **1 mark** for **two** correct answers | 1 |
| 19 | G5.5 – commas in lists | tick: to separate items in a list | | 1 |
| 20 | G6.1 – synonyms and antonyms | tick: separate | | 1 |
| 21 | G1.9 - Subject and object | **Accept:**<br>The football manager posed for a photograph.<br>The football manager posed for a photograph.<br>The football manager posed for a photograph. | | 1 |

| 22 | G5.10 – colons | tick: We saw beautiful landscapes on our trip: mountains, lakes and coasts. | | 1 |
|---|---|---|---|---|
| 23 | G2.3 – commands | tick: Bring a packed lunch so you do not get hungry. | | 1 |
| 24 | G3.4 – subordinating conjunctions and subordinate clauses | circle: even though it might be a little scary at first | | 1 |
| 25 | G3.4 – subordinating conjunctions and subordinate clauses G1.7 – prepositions, G1.4 – conjunctions | tick: I'd like to finish my book before we go out. The phone stopped ringing before I could answer it. | **1 mark** for **two** correct answers | 1 |
| 26 | **G1.5 – pronouns** | circle: his; He; them | **1 mark** for **three** correct answers | 1 |
| 27 | **G6.1 – synonyms and antonyms** | influence    persuade<br>courteous    polite<br>confine    imprison<br>accusation    blame<br>thanks    gratitude | **1 mark** for **five** correct answers | 1 |
| 28 | **G1.3 - Adjectives, G1.6 - Adverbs** | careful - Adjective<br>carefully - Adverb | No spelling requirements | 1 |
| 29 | **G4.1b – verbs in perfect form** | had | | 1 |
| 30 | **G4.3 – subjunctive verb forms** | tick: I would drive more slowly if I were you. | | 1 |
| 31 | **G1.6a – adverbials** | underline: During the match | **Accept** other means of indicating the answer, e.g. circling. | 1 |
| 32 | **G5.14 – bullet points** | **Accept** in any order:<br>• scissors<br>• coloured paper<br>• glue | **Also accept** capitalisation of the three items and/or consistent use of commas or semi-colons after the first two items if accompanied by a full stop after the third.<br><br>**Do not accept** inconsistent use of punctuation or capitalisation. | 1 |
| 33 | **G1.5 – pronouns** | tick: pronouns | | 1 |
| 34 | **G4.1a – simple past and simple present** | walked; sang; brought | **1 mark** for **three** correct answers.<br>Answer must be lower case and correctly spelled. | 1 |

| 35 | G5.1 – capital letters | tick: The teacher took the children to the library in the middle of Newcastle. | | 1 |
|---|---|---|---|---|
| 36 | G2.2 – questions | tick: Can you tell me what time it opens at | | 1 |
| 37 | G1.5a – possessive pronouns | circle: her | | 1 |
| 38 | G3.2 - Noun phrases | **Accept:**<br>Noun phrase<br>Expanded noun phrase<br>Complement | No spelling requirements | 1 |
| 39 | G1.2 – verbs | tick: Can you light the candles please? | | 1 |
| 40 | G2.1 – statements;<br>G2.2 – questions;<br>G2.3 – commands;<br>G2.4 – exclamations | You have been to that art gallery, haven't you    question<br><br>The art gallery is open now    statement<br><br>How amazing the art is in this gallery    exclamation<br><br>Go into the gift shop in the gallery    command | **1 mark** for **four** correct answers | 1 |
| 41 | G6.2 – prefixes | im | Must be correctly spelled. | 1 |
| 42 | G1.7 – prepositions | tick: He walked across the road.<br>We struggled to climb over the fence. | **1 mark** for **two** correct answers | 1 |
| 43a | G5.9 – punctuation for parenthesis | commas | | 1 |
| 43b | G5.9 – punctuation for parenthesis | brackets or dashes | Accept either answer. | 1 |
| 44 | G5.11 – semi-colons | There will be a huge celebration party next week; it will probably be on Monday. | | 1 |
| 45 | G3.2 – noun phrases | **Accept** answers that are a noun phrase which include three words, for example:<br>My friend Claire<br>Your little brother | Capital letters must be used where appropriate. | 1 |
| 46 | G1.5a - Possessive pronouns | circle: his | | 1 |
| 47 | G4.4 – passive and active | The children planted the seeds. | The answer must be correctly punctuated.<br><br>**Do not accept** answers with omitted words or additional words. | 1 |
| 48 | G6.1 – synonyms and antonyms | circle: overpriced, extortionate | **1 mark** for **two** correct answers | 1 |
| 49 | G4.1b – verbs in perfect form | tick: My dog was unwell, but since he has been at the vet's, he is much better. | | 1 |

# Test 2, Paper 2: spelling task transcript

Spelling one: The word is **creased**.
That jacket is too **creased** to wear.

Spelling two: The word is **families**.
Our **families** are all getting together for a big meal.

Spelling three: The word is **environment**.
It is important to care for the **environment**.

Spelling four: The word is **appearing**.
The same bird keeps **appearing** at my window.

Spelling five: The word is **mature**.
There are **mature** trees of a hundred years old in the park.

Spelling six: The word is **collapsed**.
The bridge **collapsed** during the flood.

Spelling seven: The word is **deliberate**.
James made a **deliberate** effort to work harder.

Spelling eight: The word is **illogical**.
It would be **illogical** to make a mistake on purpose.

Spelling nine: The word is **handkerchief**.
I need a **handkerchief** because I'm going to sneeze.

Spelling ten: The word is **tongue**.
This spicy food is making my **tongue** tingle.

Spelling eleven: The word is **infectious**.
Even a cold can be **infectious**.

Spelling twelve: The word is **panel**.
You will meet the **panel** of judges before the competition.

Spelling thirteen: The word is **attendance**.
This class has a good **attendance** record.

Spelling fourteen: The word is **invisible**.
Sam's writing is so small it is almost **invisible**.

Spelling fifteen: The word is **received**.
The twins **received** lots of gifts for their birthday.

Spelling sixteen: The word is **further**.
The guide told us not to walk any **further**.

Spelling seventeen: The word is **famous**.
A **famous** author is coming to our school next month.

Spelling eighteen: The word is **architect**.
The **architect** presented her designs to the council.

Spelling nineteen: The word is **signature**.
Leave space for your **signature** at the end of the letter.

Spelling twenty: The word is **descendant**.
We looked at the family tree to identify who Prince Charles was a **descendant** of.

# Test 3, Paper 1: questions

| Qu. | Content domain | Answer | Marking guidance | Mark |
|---|---|---|---|---|
| 1 | G5.1 – capital letters | tick: The pyrenees is a range of mountains in Spain. One of England's coasts faces the atlantic Ocean. | **1 mark** for **two** correct answers | 1 |
| 2 | G1.2 – verbs | circle: stood; passed | **1 mark** for **two** correct answers | 1 |
| 3 | G2.2 – question | has she | | 1 |
| 4 | G1.1 – nouns, G1.6 – adverbs, G1.7 – prepositions G1.8 – determiners | now (A)   otters (N)   in (P)   the (D) | **1 mark** for **four** correct answers | 1 |
| 5 | G3.4 – subordinating conjunctions and subordinate clauses | circle: until; As; while | **1 mark** for **three** correct answers | 1 |
| 6 | G1.9 – subject and object | cows (S)   grass (O)   We (S)   rattle (O) | **1 mark** for **four** correct answers | 1 |
| 7 | G5.5 - Commas in lists, G5.6a - Commas to clarify meaning | Pam's hobbies are swimming, cycling, reading and listening to music. | | 1 |

| 8 | G5.8 – apostrophes | tick: They hadn't visited Henry's house before. It's time to go home now. | **1 mark** for **two** correct answers | 1 |
|---|---|---|---|---|
| 9 | G3.2 – noun phrases | **Accept** any suitable noun phrase that makes sense, containing three words. Use capital letters where appropriate. For example: A new family; My friend Baljit. | | 1 |
| 10 | G1.8 – determiners | circle: any; the; a; some | **1 mark** for **four** correct answers | 1 |
| 11 | G4.1c – modal verbs | tick: I will travel by plane in the morning. | | 1 |
| 12 | G3.4 – subordinating conjunctions and subordinate clauses | tick: although | | 1 |
| 13 | G4.4 – passive and active | (see table below) | **1 mark** for **four** correct answers | 1 |
| 14 | G5.7 – inverted commas | tick: "Will everyone please listen?" requested Meera. | | 1 |
| 15 | G5.6a – commas to clarify meaning | tick: to mark the end of a clause | | 1 |
| 16 | G4.1d – present and past progressive | tick: Ants are marching across the floor of my kitchen. Marcus is sitting on the grass to watch the ants carrying leaves to their nest. | **1 mark** for **two** correct answers | 1 |
| 17 | G6.2 – prefixes | mis lead / dis integrate / over look / un necessary | **1 mark** for **four** correct answers | 1 |
| 18 | G5.13 – hyphens | tick: There are 300-year-old houses in my street. | | 1 |
| 19 | G5.10 – colons | We have a number of people visiting this weekend: aunts, uncles, grandparents and cousins. | | 1 |
| 20 | G3.3 - Co-ordinating conjunctions | **Accept** a grammatically correct and accurately punctuated sentence using an appropriate co-ordinating conjunction, with or without a preceding commas, e.g. and, but, yet. You can go to the cinema <u>but</u> you will need to be home by 9pm. | | 1 |
| 21 | G1.5 – pronouns | tick: his   him   them | | 1 |

Question 13 table:

| Sentence | Active | Passive |
|---|---|---|
| All of the paintings in the museum had been stolen. | | ✔ |
| The thief entered through an open window. | ✔ | |
| Some of the pictures were recovered by the police. | | ✔ |
| Unfortunately, the robber escaped with the best ones. | ✔ | |

| 22 | G3.1a – relative clauses | **Accept** answers that refer to the function of a non-defining relative clause, e.g. to add extra information, to tell us more about the cousin. | | 1 |
|---|---|---|---|---|
| 23 | G6.3 – suffixes | ness | | 1 |
| 24 | G5.12 – single dashes | tick: The tiger is the biggest species of the cat family – it can reach lengths of up to 3.3 metres. | | 1 |

| 25 | G5.11 – semi-colons | | **1 mark** for **three** correct answers | 1 |
|---|---|---|---|---|

| Sentence | Correct | Incorrect |
|---|---|---|
| Trekking through a jungle can be very hard work; pushing through bushes, climbing over creepers. | | ✔ |
| The tops of mountains can have extreme climates; they can be extremely hot, or extremely cold. | ✔ | |
| Surprisingly, a desert supports many types of plant; and wildlife. | | ✔ |

| 26 | G4.1d – present and past progressive | were running | **Accept** minor slips in spelling. | 1 |
|---|---|---|---|---|
| 27 | G4.4 – passive and active | A lovely solo was played on the piano by Alex.<br>A lovely solo was played by Alex on the piano.<br>A lovely solo was played. | **Accept** answers that omit 'lovely', and those that have minor slips in spelling. | 1 |
| 28 | G4.1c – modal verbs | **Accept** answers that explain that the event is less likely to take place, e.g. *might* means that it is not definite. | | 1 |
| 29 | G5.9 – punctuation for parenthesis | Golden eagles have been known to attack a variety of large animals (foxes, wild cats, deer and even goats) using their large talons and beaks. | | 1 |
| 30 | G6.1 – synonyms and antonyms | tick: cover   surround | | 1 |
| 31 | G3.4 – subordinating conjunctions and subordinate clauses | underline: if they are caught by predators | | 1 |

| 32 | G1.7 – prepositions, G3.4 – subordinating conjunctions and subordinate clauses | | | **1 mark** for **three** correct answers | 1 |
|---|---|---|---|---|---|

| Sentence | Subordinating conjunction | Preposition |
|---|---|---|
| Shall we go to the museum <u>after</u> we have seen the castle? | ✔ | |
| The concert will begin <u>after</u> everyone has sat down. | ✔ | |
| Let's make some cakes <u>after</u> school today. | | ✔ |

| 33 | G1.8 – determiners | We went to a farm and I collected an apple.<br><br>We all had a fantastic time.<br><br>I hope we can go to the farm again. | **1 mark** for **three** correct answers | 1 |
|---|---|---|---|---|
| 34 | G1.1 – nouns | tick: nouns | | 1 |
| 35 | G1.6a - Adverbials | <u>In November</u>, our class will go away on a residential trip. | | 1 |
| 36 | G5.8 – apostrophes | He is<br><br>I will<br><br>do not | **1 mark** for **three** correct answers.<br><br>Answers must be correctly spelled. | 1 |
| 37 | G5.6b – commas after fronted adverbials | tick: After half-term, swimming lessons | | 1 |
| 38 | G3.4 – subordinating conjunctions and subordinate clauses | **Accept** answers with an appropriate subordinating conjunction: because | Answer must be lower case and correctly spelled. | 1 |
| 39 | G4.2 – tense consistency | circle: was, went | | 1 |
| 40 | G3.1a – relative clauses | underline: who sits next to me | | 1 |
| 41 | G1.2 – verbs | tick: Don't point, it's rude. | | 1 |
| 42 | G2.3 – commands | **Accept** an answer that is a plausible command. | Answer must be correctly punctuated with either a full stop or an exclamation mark. | 1 |
| 43 | G2.1 – statements | tick: You can carry the equipment with a partner | | 1 |
| 44 | G1.6 – adverbs | circle: soon | | 1 |
| 45 | G2.4 – exclamations | tick: How amazing that present is | | 1 |
| 46 | G7.4 – the subjunctive | tick: were | | 1 |
| 47 | G3.2 – noun phrases | tick: as a noun phrase | | 1 |
| 48 | G6.3 – suffixes | foxes<br><br>lorry<br><br>cacti / catuses | **1 mark** for **three** correct answers.<br><br>Answers must be lower case and correctly spelled. | 1 |
| 49 | G4.4 – passive and active | (see table below) | **1 mark** for **three** correct answers | 1 |
| 50 | G6.2 – prefixes | mis | | 1 |

Table for item 49:

| Sentence | Active | Passive |
|---|---|---|
| The girls won the trophy. | ✔ | |
| Everybody was surprised when they won. | ✔ | |
| The winning goal was scored by Jess. | | ✔ |

# Test 3, Paper 2: spelling task transcript

Spelling one: The word is **clapped**.
Everyone **clapped** at the end of the performance.

Spelling two: The word is **difficulty**.
Jo had no **difficulty** in climbing to the top of the rope.

Spelling three: The word is **imaginative**.
That's a very **imaginative** idea.

Spelling four: The word is **surrounded**.
The park is **surrounded** by bushes and trees.

Spelling five: The word is **creating**.
We are **creating** a massive collage in class.

Spelling six: The word is **weighs**.
That bag **weighs** too much for me to carry.

Spelling seven: The word is **irrelevant**.
Charlie's idea was **irrelevant** to the discussion.

Spelling eight: The word is **shoulder**.
Anna carries her bag over her **shoulder**.

Spelling nine: The word is **international**.
England has several **international** airports.

Spelling ten: The word is **probably**.
We will **probably** have a roast dinner at the weekend.

Spelling eleven: The word is **possession**.
If you have a phone in your **possession**, turn it off now.

Spelling twelve: The word is **knuckle**.
I grazed my **knuckle** when I fell over.

Spelling thirteen: The word is **conquered**.
The Romans **conquered** much of Europe.

Spelling fourteen: The word is **scenery**.
I am helping to make the **scenery** for the school play.

Spelling fifteen: The word is **neighbour**.
My **neighbour** has lost her cat.

Spelling sixteen: The word is **doubt**.
Since you have missed the train, I **doubt** you will be on time.

Spelling seventeen: The word is **transferred**.
She **transferred** everything from the boxes into the new office.

Spelling eighteen: The word is **typical**.
It was a **typical** week for Luke.

Spelling nineteen: The word is **vague**.
She had a **vague** memory of her holiday in Spain.

Spelling twenty: The word is **adventurous**.
After the residential, Sarah was known as the most **adventurous** girl.

**22** Which sentence below is correctly punctuated?

Tick **one**.

1 mark

We saw beautiful landscapes: on our trip, mountains, lakes and coasts. ☐

We saw beautiful landscapes on our trip: mountains, lakes and coasts. ☐

We saw: beautiful landscapes on our trip, mountains, lakes and coasts. ☐

We saw beautiful landscapes on our trip, mountains: lakes and coasts. ☐

**23** Which sentence is a **command**?

Tick **one**.

1 mark

I am bringing a packed lunch. ☐

You should bring a packed lunch. ☐

Bring a packed lunch so you do not get hungry. ☐

You will need a packed lunch so you do not get hungry. ☐

**24** Circle the **subordinate clause** in the sentence below.

1 mark

I would love to swim with dolphins even though it might be a little scary at first.

/3

*Total for this page*

31

**25** Which sentences below use <u>before</u> as a **subordinating conjunction**?

Tick **two**.

1 mark

Let's go to the swimming pool <u>before</u> lunch. ☐

I'd like to finish my book <u>before</u> we go out. ☐

Can we practise our dance again <u>before</u> the performance? ☐

The phone stopped ringing <u>before</u> I could answer it. ☐

**26** Circle all the **pronouns** in the passage below.

Archie took a lot of care with his toys. He was annoyed because one of them had been broken by a friend.

1 mark

**27** Match the words below with their **synonyms**.

1 mark

| influence | imprison |
| courteous | polite |
| confine | persuade |
| accusation | gratitude |
| thanks | blame |

/3

*Total for this page*

**28** What is the **word class** of each underlined word?

Baljit drew a <u>careful</u> picture. _____

Baljit draws <u>carefully</u>. _____

**29** The audience finished their applause for the magician before the singer began.

Complete the sentence below with the correct **verb form**.

The audience _____ finished applauding the musician just as the singer took her place on stage.

**30** Which sentence below uses the **subjunctive form**?

Tick **one**.

Everyone in our family would like to go on an African safari. ☐

I would drive more slowly if I were you. ☐

Josh will meet you at the front of the swimming pool. ☐

Musah would like to have a new bike for his birthday. ☐

**31** Underline the **adverbial phrase** in the sentence below.

During the match, Katie scored two amazing goals.

1 mark

**32** Priya is making a collage picture. She needs to use scissors, coloured paper and glue.

Finish the instructions below, writing the equipment as a list with **bullet points**.

Remember to punctuate your answer correctly.

To make a collage, you will need this equipment:

- _____

- _____

- _____

1 mark

**33** What is the **word class** of the underlined words?

<u>We</u> waited patiently for <u>him</u> as <u>he</u> was really late.

Tick **one**.

prepositions ☐

verbs ☐

pronouns ☐

nouns ☐

1 mark

/3

*Total for this page*

34

**34** Write the verbs in the gaps in the **simple past tense**.

to walk

The bus didn't come so we _____ to school.

to sing                              to bring

My friend _____ with the choir while I _____
more chairs for the audience to sit on.

1 mark

**35** Which sentence uses **capital letters** correctly?

Tick **one**.

1 mark

The Teacher took the children to the library in the
middle of Newcastle. ☐

The teacher took the children to the Library in the
middle of newcastle. ☐

The Teacher took the children to the Library in the
middle of Newcastle. ☐

The teacher took the children to the library in the
middle of Newcastle. ☐

**36** Tick the option that must end with a **question mark**.

Tick **one**.

1 mark

Ask me what time it opens at ☐

Can you tell me what time it opens at ☐

What time it opens at is written on the sign ☐

I will ask what time it opens at ☐

/3

*Total for
this page*

35

**37** Circle the **possessive pronoun** in the passage below.

When I visited the new school, a girl showed me where

her locker was.

1 mark

**38** What is the grammatical term for the underlined words in the sentence below?

She carried <u>the heavy wooden chest with a gold handle</u> into the kitchen.

_____

1 mark

**39** Which sentence uses the word <u>light</u> as a **verb**?

Tick **one**.

| | |
|---|---|
| There was a very bright light in the distance. | ☐ |
| Can you light the candles please? | ☐ |
| I need a new light for the kitchen. | ☐ |
| The light was on all night. | ☐ |

1 mark

/3

*Total for this page*

**40** Draw a line to match each sentence to its correct **function**. Use each function box only once.

| 1 mark |

**Sentence**                                                    **Function**

| You have been to that art gallery, haven't you |         | command |

| The art gallery is open now |                            | exclamation |

| How amazing the art is in this gallery |                | statement |

| Go into the gift shop in the gallery |                   | question |

**41** Which one **prefix** can be added to all three words below to make their **antonyms**?

| 1 mark |

Write the prefix in the box.

mature
moral
patient

| |

**42** Which two sentences contain a **preposition**?

| 1 mark |

                                                    Tick **two**.

She happily watched the concert.                    ☐

He walked across the road.                          ☐

The books were arranged neatly.                     ☐

We struggled to climb over the fence.               ☐

| /3 |

*Total for this page*   **37**

**43a** What is the name of the **punctuation marks** on either side of the words <u>which was broken</u> in the sentence below?

1 mark

Dad put the bottle, which was broken, into the bin.

_____

**43b** What is the name of a **different** punctuation mark that could be used correctly in the same places?

1 mark

_____

**44** Insert a **semi-colon** in the correct place in the sentence below.

There will be a huge celebration party next week it will

1 mark

probably be on Monday.

/3

Total for
this page

**45** Write a **noun phrase** containing at least three words to complete the sentence below.

Remember to punctuate your sentence correctly.

_____ is coming to my party on Wednesday.

1 mark

**46** Circle the **possessive pronoun** in the sentence below.

Luke took some of Ellie's sweets and then pretended that

they were his.

1 mark

**47** Rewrite the sentence below so that it is in the **active voice**.

Remember to punctuate your sentence correctly.

The seeds were planted by the children.

_____

1 mark

/ 3

*Total for this page*

**48** Circle the **two** words that are **synonyms** in the passage below.

Many of the items in the shop were overpriced. They tried
to find some more reasonable gifts, but left feeling
everything was extortionate.

1 mark

**49** Which sentence uses the **present perfect form**?

Tick **one**.

1 mark

My dog was unwell, but since he has been at the
vet's, he is much better. ☐

He was feeling excited when he won the cup. ☐

The children hung up their coats and sat in their seats. ☐

They are playing their instruments in the orchestra
this evening. ☐

/2

*Total for
this page*

| Name: | Class: | Date: | Total marks: | /20 |

# Test 2, Paper 2: spelling

1   That jacket is too _____ to wear.

2   Our _____ are all getting together for a big meal.

3   It is important to care for the _____.

4   The same bird keeps _____ at my window.

5   There are _____ trees of a hundred years old in the park.

6   The bridge _____ during the flood.

7   James made a _____ effort to work harder.

8   It would be _____ to make a mistake on purpose.

9   I need a _____ because I'm going to sneeze.

10   This spicy food is making my _____ tingle.

11   Even a cold can be _____.

12   You will meet the _____ of judges before the competition.

13   This class has a good _____ record.

14   Sam's writing is so small it is almost _____.

15   The twins _____ lots of gifts for their birthday.

16   The guide told us not to walk any _____.

17   A _____ author is coming to our school next month.

18   The _____ presented her designs to the council.

19   Leave space for your _____ at the end of the letter.

20   We looked at the family tree to identify who Prince Charles was a _____ of.

| Name: | Class: | Date: | Total marks: | /50 |

# Test 3, Paper 1: questions

**1** Which of the sentences below have a **capital letter** missing?

Tick **two**.

1 mark

We often build snowmen in the winter. ☐

I went to see the dentist about my toothache. ☐

The pyrenees is a range of mountains in Spain. ☐

One of England's coasts faces the atlantic Ocean. ☐

**2** Circle all the **verbs** in the sentence below.

Traffic stood still as the procession passed through the

centre of town.

1 mark

**3** Add a question tag at the end of the sentence below to make it a **question**.

Sarah hasn't arrived yet, _____ _____?

1 mark

/3

*Total for this page*

**4** Label the boxes with **D (determiner)**, **A (adverb)**, **N (noun)** or **P (preposition)** to show the parts of the sentence.

Now our river is much cleaner, otters have come back to live in

the area.

1 mark

**5** Circle all the **conjunctions** in the passage below.

The explorers had followed the path until they met a river.

As they could not cross it, they sat down on the bank while

they considered a plan.

1 mark

**6** Label the boxes with **S (subject)** or **O (object)** in the sentences below.

The cows are contentedly munching grass in their field.

We shook the rattle and the baby laughed.

1 mark

/3

*Total for this page*  (43)

**7** Add two **commas** to the sentence below to make it clear that Pam has four hobbies.

Pam's hobbies are swimming cycling reading and listening to music.

1 mark

**8** Tick all the sentences that correctly use **apostrophes**.

Teri didn't like the snake's at the zoo. ☐

Ahmed always enjoy's eating biscuits and cakes. ☐

They hadn't visited Henry's house before. ☐

It's time to go home now. ☐

1 mark

**9** Write a **noun phrase** containing at least three words to complete the sentence below.

Remember to punctuate your sentence correctly.

_____ has moved in next door to us.

1 mark

/3

Total for this page

**10** Circle all the **determiners** in the passage below.

Do we have any biscuits in the cupboard? If there is a

packet, can I have some?

**11** Which of the events in the sentences below is **most likely** to happen?

Tick **one**.

We could build a tunnel through the mountain. ☐

They might be able to cross the river further downstream. ☐

I will travel by plane in the morning. ☐

She may call you this weekend. ☐

**12** Which option correctly introduces the **subordinate clause** in the sentence below?

The winter's evening was very cold indeed _____ the fire was burning brightly to try to keep us warm.

Tick **one**.

in addition ☐

instead of ☐

although ☐

however ☐

**13** Tick one box in each row to show whether the sentences are written in the **active voice** or the **passive voice**.

| Sentence | Active | Passive |
|---|---|---|
| All of the paintings in the museum had been stolen. | | |
| The thief entered through an open window. | | |
| Some of the pictures were recovered by the police. | | |
| Unfortunately, the robber escaped with the best ones. | | |

1 mark

**14** Which sentence is correctly punctuated?

Tick **one**.

"Will everyone please listen? requested Meera." ☐

"Will everyone please listen? requested" Meera. ☐

"Will everyone please listen"? requested Meera. ☐

"Will everyone please listen?" requested Meera. ☐

1 mark

**15** Why is a **comma** used in the sentence below?

Whenever we go for a walk at the coast, we collect interesting shells and stones in a bucket.

Tick **one**.

to separate items in a list ☐

to divide the sentence in half ☐

to mark the end of a clause ☐

to join two sentences together ☐

1 mark

/3

*Total for this page*

**16** Tick two sentences that include verbs in the **present progressive form**.

Tick **two**.

1 mark

Ants have six legs and each leg has six joints. ☐

Although tiny, ants can lift 20 times their own body weight. ☐

Ants are marching across the floor of my kitchen. ☐

Marcus is sitting on the grass to watch the ants carrying leaves to their nest. ☐

**17** Draw a line to match the correct **prefix** with each of the words below.

1 mark

| mis | integrate |
| dis | look |
| over | lead |
| un | necessary |

**18** Tick one box to show the sentence that describes the houses that are 300 years old.

Tick **one**.

1 mark

There are 300 year-old houses in my street. ☐

There are 300 year old houses in my street. ☐

There are 300-year-old houses in my street. ☐

There are 300 year old-houses in my street. ☐

/3

*Total for this page*

47

**19** Insert a **colon** in the correct place to the sentence below.

We have a number of people visiting this weekend aunts,

uncles, grandparents and cousins.

1 mark

**20** Rewrite the two sentences below as one sentence using an appropriate **coordinating conjunction**.

Remember to punctuate your answer correctly.

You can go to the cinema. You will need to be home by 9pm.

_____

1 mark

**21** Tick one box to show which **pronouns** should complete this sentence.

The instructions were so difficult to follow that he had to

ask _____ brother to help _____ with

_____.

Tick **one**.

| | | | |
|---|---|---|---|
| he | her | those | ☐ |
| his | him | them | ☐ |
| her | them | it | ☐ |
| my | his | they | ☐ |

1 mark

/3

Total for
this page

**22** Explain why the words underlined are placed between a pair of **commas**.

My cousin, <u>who used to work in India</u>, is moving to a new job in England.

---

**23** Add a **suffix** to change the word <u>forgive</u> into a noun.

I will <u>forgive</u> you.

You have my <u>forgive</u> _____.

---

**24** Which of the sentences below correctly uses a **single dash**?

Tick **one**.

The tiger is the biggest species of the cat family – it can reach lengths of up to 3.3 metres. ☐

Tigers are endangered by hunting – and destruction of their environments. ☐

Tiger cubs leave their mothers – at about two years old. ☐

Tigers can reach speeds of up to 40 miles an hour – when hunting. ☐

**25** Tick one box in each row to show whether a **semi-colon** is used correctly or incorrectly.

1 mark

| Sentence | Correct | Incorrect |
|---|---|---|
| Trekking through a jungle can be very hard work; pushing through bushes, climbing over creepers. | | |
| The tops of mountains can have extreme climates; they can be extremely hot, or extremely cold. | | |
| Surprisingly, a desert supports many types of plant; and wildlife. | | |

**26** Rewrite the underlined verb in the **past progressive**.

While we <u>to run</u> for the bus, I tripped and fell.

1 mark

**27** Rewrite the sentence below, using the **passive voice**.

Remember to punctuate your answer correctly.

Alex played a lovely solo on the piano.

1 mark

_____

_____

/3

*Total for this page*

**28** Explain how the word <u>might</u> changes the meaning of the sentence.

I will practise my spellings before the test.

I <u>might</u> practise my spellings before the test.

_____

_____

_____

1 mark

**29** Correctly insert a pair of **brackets** in the sentence below.

Golden eagles have been known to attack a variety of large animals foxes, wild cats, deer and even goats using their large talons and beaks.

1 mark

**30** Tick the words that mean the same as <u>envelop</u>.

Tick **one**.

| | | |
|---|---|---|
| cover | surround | ☐ |
| send | communicate | ☐ |
| locate | find | ☐ |
| present | display | ☐ |

1 mark

/3

*Total for this page*

51

**31** Underline the **subordinate clause** in the sentence below.

Some lizards can detach their tails if they are caught by predators.

1 mark

**32** Tick one box in each row to show whether the word <u>after</u> is used as a **subordinating conjunction** or as a **preposition**.

| Sentence | Subordinating conjunction | Preposition |
|---|---|---|
| Shall we go to the museum <u>after</u> we have seen the castle? | | |
| The concert will begin <u>after</u> everyone has sat down. | | |
| Let's make some cakes <u>after</u> school today. | | |

1 mark

**33** Draw a line to match each sentence to the correct **determiner**.

Use each determiner only **once**.

| We went to a farm and I collected _____ apple. | | the |
|---|---|---|
| We all had _____ fantastic time. | | a |
| I hope we can go to _____ farm again. | | an |

1 mark

/3

*Total for this page*

52

**34** What is the **word class** of the underlined words in the sentence below?

We saw a very unusual <u>bird</u> while on holiday in <u>Wales</u>.

**Tick one.**

adjectives ☐

adverbs ☐

pronouns ☐

nouns ☐

1 mark

**35** Underline the **adverbial** in the sentence below.

In November, our class will go away on a residential trip.

1 mark

**36** Replace the underlined words in the sentences below with their **expanded forms**.

<u>He's</u> going to meet me after dinner, so <u>I'll</u> make sure I am on time.

_____          _____

I really <u>don't</u> want to be late.

_____

1 mark

/3

*Total for this page*

53

**37** Tick the option that correctly completes the sentence below.

_____ will take place on Fridays at 1:30 p.m.

Tick **one**.

After half-term swimming, lessons ☐

After half-term, swimming lessons ☐

After, half-term swimming lessons ☐

After half-term, swimming lessons, ☐

1 mark

**38** Complete the sentence with an appropriate **subordinating conjunction**.

We cannot go swimming today _____ it is too cold.

1 mark

**39** Circle the **two** words that show the **tense** in the sentence below.

The zoo was shut, so we went to the cinema instead.

1 mark

/ 3

*Total for this page*

**40** Underline the **relative clause** in the sentence below.

The girl who sits next to me is called Jackie.

1 mark

**41** Which sentence uses the word <u>point</u> as a **verb**?

Tick **one**.

| | |
|---|---|
| What was the point in that? | ☐ |
| My pencil has an extremely sharp point. | ☐ |
| Don't point, it's rude. | ☐ |
| Place the ruler next to the point. | ☐ |

1 mark

**42** Write a **command** which could be the first step in the instructions for getting ready for bed.

Remember to punctuate your answer correctly.

_____

_____

1 mark

/3

*Total for this page*

55

**43** Which sentence is a **statement**?

Tick **one**.

Do not lift that equipment by yourself ☐

Be careful when you lift the equipment ☐

You can carry the equipment with a partner ☐

Do you know how to carry the equipment ☐

1 mark

**44** Circle the **adverb** in the sentence below.

I really love to travel and hope I can go to Italy soon.

1 mark

**45** Tick the option that must end with an **exclamation mark**.

Tick **one**.

How amazing that present is ☐

How did you manage to do that ☐

Give it to me ☐

Stand up ☐

1 mark

/3

*Total for
this page*

**46** Which **verb** completes the sentence so that it uses the **subjunctive form**?

I wish I _____ able to come, but I already have plans.

Tick **one**.

were ☐

be ☐

am ☐

was ☐

**47** What is the grammatical term for the underlined words in the sentence below?

The multi-coloured kites were very popular on the beach.

Tick **one**.

as an adverbial ☐

as a noun phrase ☐

as a subordinate clause ☐

as a fronted adverbial ☐

1 mark

**48** Complete the table below with the correct **singular** or **plural** form.

one <u>fox</u> ⟶ seven _____

one _____ ⟶ some <u>lorries</u>

one <u>cactus</u> ⟶ several _____

1 mark

/3

*Total for this page* 57

**49** Tick one box in each row to show whether the sentence is written in the **active voice** or the **passive voice**.

| Sentence | Active | Passive |
|---|---|---|
| The girls won the trophy. | | |
| Everybody was surprised when they won. | | |
| The winning goal was scored by Jess. | | |

1 mark

**50** Which one **prefix** can be added to all three words below to make their **antonyms**?

Write the prefix in the box.

understanding

read

spell

1 mark

/2

*Total for this page*

| Name: | Class: | Date: | Total marks: | /20 |

# Test 3, Paper 2: spelling

1   Everyone _____ at the end of the performance. ☐

2   Jo had no _____ in climbing to the top of the rope. ☐

3   That's a very _____ idea. ☐

4   The park is _____ by bushes and trees. ☐

5   We are _____ a massive collage in class. ☐

6   That bag _____ too much for me to carry. ☐

7   Charlie's idea was _____ to the discussion. ☐

8   Anna carries her bag over her _____. ☐

9   England has several _____ airports. ☐

10   We will _____ have a roast dinner at the weekend. ☐

11   If you have a phone in your _____, turn it off now. ☐

12   I grazed my _____ when I fell over. ☐

13   The Romans _____ much of Europe. ☐

14   I am helping to make the _____ for the school play. ☐

15   My _____ has lost her cat. ☐

16   Since you have missed the train, I _____ you will be on time. ☐

17   She _____ everything from the boxes into the new office. ☐

18   It was a _____ week for Luke. ☐

19   She had a _____ memory of her holiday in Spain. ☐

20   After the residential, Sarah was known as the most _____ girl. ☐

# General guidance on marking Paper 1

## Selected response questions

In questions where children must select the correct response or identify a feature from a given field of data (such as tick boxes and tables, circling or underlining of the answer, drawing lines to 'match' boxes, labelling, e.g. 'V' for 'verb'):

- Accept any unambiguous indication of the correct answer (e.g. answer circled rather than ticked; lines that do not touch the boxes, provided the intention is clear).
- Do not accept encircling/underlining of less than half of the required word.
- Do not accept ambiguous labelling (e.g. the use of 'AD' or 'A' where a distinction is required between 'adjective' and 'adverb').

## Constructed response questions

In open questions or questions where children must transform a given word, phrase or sentence, or insert a word or phrase:

- Accept incorrect spellings of the correct response if no specific mark scheme guidance is given. Correct spelling is generally required for questions assessing contracted forms, plurals, verb tenses, prefixes and suffixes.
- Do not accept punctuation that is ambiguous or not recognisable as the required punctuation mark, for example if it is unclear whether the mark is a comma or full stop.
- When punctuating a sentence, do not accept answers in which capital letters are omitted or placed inappropriately in a sentence, or where an entire word is capitalised, nor answers where there is ambiguity in the comparative sizes of letters.
- Accept letters or punctuation marks that have been reversed, but which are still clearly identifiable.
- Accept correct answers that replace a crossed-out attempt, but not crossed-out answers, whether or not these have been replaced by a further attempt.

## All question types

- Accept a correct answer given somewhere other than the answer space, providing it is not contradicted by another answer written elsewhere.
- Do not accept an answer when more than the required number of answers is given (e.g. both correct and incorrect responses given).